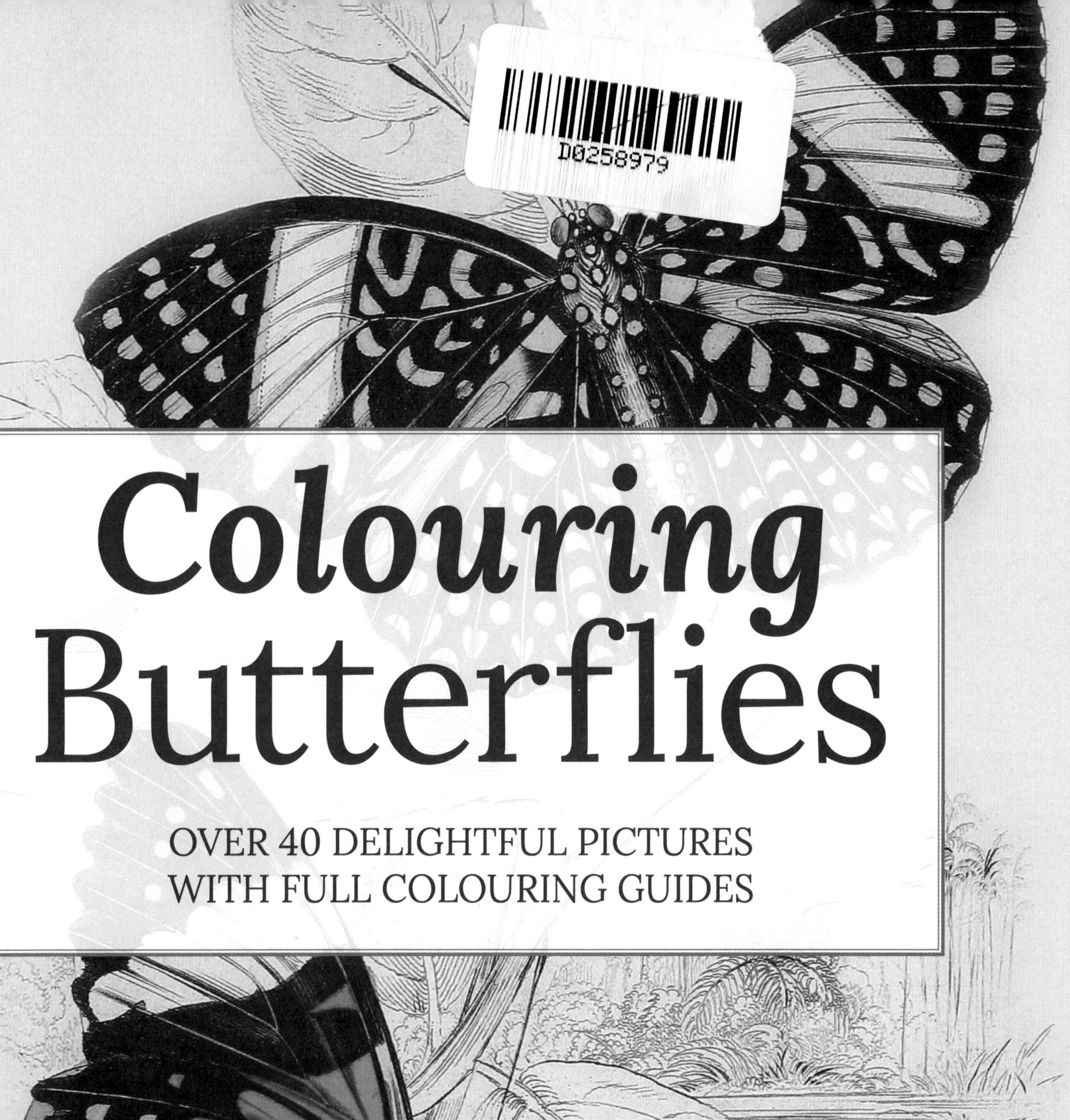

# Colouring Butterflies

OVER 40 DELIGHTFUL PICTURES
WITH FULL COLOURING GUIDES

ARCTURUS

This edition published in 2016 by Arcturus Publishing Limited
26/27 Bickels Yard, 151–153 Bermondsey Street,
London SE1 3HA



ISBN: 978-1-78404-852-5
CH004681UK
Supplier 29, Date 1215, Print Run 4896

Printed in China

# Introduction

Artists have been attracted to butterflies for centuries – in fact they even appear among prehistoric Pyrenean cave paintings and on Minoan artefacts from 4,000 years ago. It wasn't just their beauty that made them important in the ancient world, for they were also regarded as spirits and in ancient Greece they were linked to the human soul.

Many artists and naturalists over the years have devoted time to making beautiful, painstaking depictions of the intricate markings and jewelled colours of butterfly wings. The plates in this book come from *The Naturalist's Library*, which was edited by the great Scottish naturalist Sir William Jardine (1800–1874) and issued in a set of 40 volumes with more than 1,300 engraved plates. Exquisitely rendered, the butterflies are shown in their natural habitat, set against the flora where you might expect to find them in the wild. The illustrations were engraved by William Lizars (1788–1859).

It would be impossible to paint a butterfly in detail from life, since they come to rest only briefly. This makes them an ideal subject for a colouring book, where time is unlimited to study their patterns and colorations. There was a time when colouring in was regarded as something strictly for children, but today adults too have discovered the enjoyment of this form of art, where all the attention is devoted to colour without worrying about getting a drawing right first. We know now, too, how relaxing it is for the mind to be focused on one absorbing activity, shutting out the stresses of life.

The choice of art materials is now very wide, and you can work with oil-based, wax-based or watersoluble colour pencils – an easy way to start. You can use them dry, blending them with your finger or a paper stump, or dilute them with oil, or water for the watersoluble pencils. Should you wish to paint, a small watercolour set and a medium-sized round brush is all you need. Whichever you choose, you'll find huge enjoyment from colouring in these beautiful butterflies.

Diana Vowles

# Key: List of plates

**1** *1 & 2 Pieris epicharis*
*3 P. philyra*

**2** *1 Leptocircus curius*
*2 Thais medesicaste*

**3** *1 Papilio protesilaus*
*2 P. sinon*

**4** *1 Marius thetis*
*2 Fabius hippona*

**5** *1 & 2 Polyommatus venus*
*3 & 4 P. achaeus*

**6** *Thaliura rhipheus*

**7** *1 Argynnis adippe*
*2 A. lathonia*

**8** *1 & 2 Polyommatus Marsyas*
*3 & 4 P. endymion*

**9** *Rhipheus dasycephalus*

**10** *1 Deiopeia bella 2 Cydosia nobilitella 3 Chloridea rhexiae 4 Alaria gaurae 5 Caterpillar*

**11** *1 Gonepteryx rhamni*
*2 Colias edusa*

**12** *1 & 2 Helicopis gnidus*
*3 Erycina octavius*

**13** *1 Nymphalis ethiocles*
*2 & 3 N. tiridates*

**14** *1 Peridromia arethusa*
*2 P. amphinome*

**15** *1 Heleona fenestrata*
*2 Anthomyza teresia*

**16** *1 Colias hyale*
*2 C. europome*

**17** *Cethosia cyane*

**18** *1 Heliconia erato*
*2 H. cynisca*
*3 H. sylvana*

**19** *1 Melitaea athalia,* var.
*2 M. artemis*
*3 M. silene*

**20** *1 Papilio ascanius*
*2 P. paris*

**21** *1 & 2 Heliconia flora*
*3 H. diaphana*
*4 Acraea pasiphae*

**22** *1 Argynnis paphia*
*2 Melitaea cinxia*

**23** *Charaxes jasius*

**24** *1 & 2 Limacodes micilia*
*3, 4, 5 Doratifera vulnerans*

**25** *1 Euploea limniace*
*2 E. plexippe*

**26** *Hipparchia semele*
*1 Male 2 Female*
*3 H. megara*

**27** *1 Callidryas eubule*
*with caterpillar & chrysalis*
*4 Terias mexicana*

**28** *1 Lycaena chryseis*
*2 L. hippothoe*
*3 L. phlaeas*

**29** *1 Pieris belisama*
*2 Anthocharis danai*
*3 Iphias leucippe*

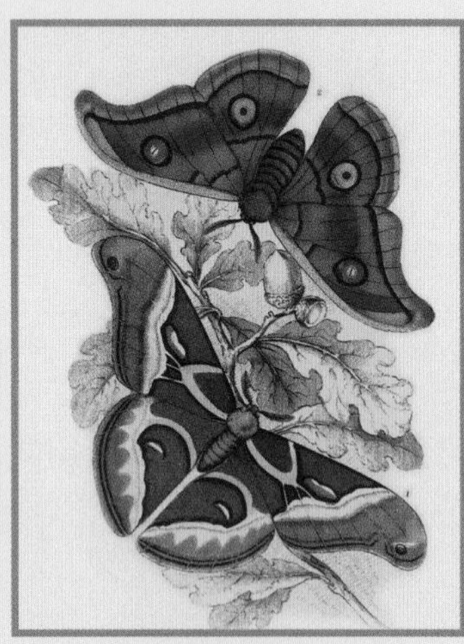

**30** *1 Saturnia cynthia*
*2 S. mylitta*

**31** *1 Polyommatus argiolus*
*Male 2 Female*
*3 P. alsus 4 P. acis*

**32** *1 Vanessa atalanta*
*2 Limenitis camilla*

**33** *1 Papilio machaon*
*2 P. podalirius*

**34** *1 & 2 Catochala neogama*
*3 C. amesia*

**35** *1 Urania sloanus*
*2 U. leilus*

**36** *1 Polyommatus arion*
*2 P. alcon*
*3 P. corydon*

**37** *Cethosia dido*

**38** *Caterpillars*

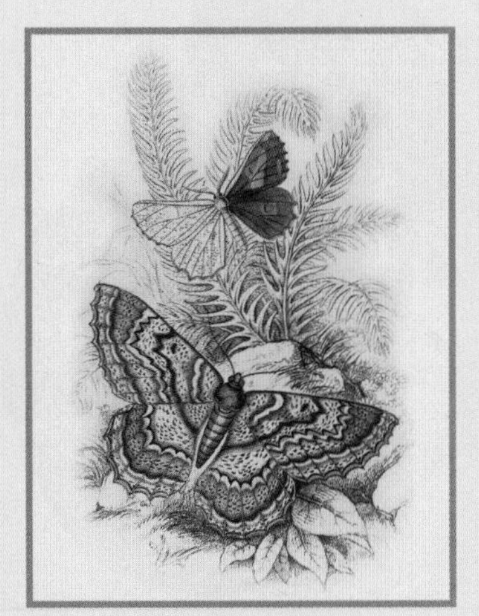

**39** *1 Angerona prunaria*
*2 Alcis scolopacea*

**40** *1 Agarista picta*
*2 Eusemia lectrix*
*3 E. maculatrix*

**41** *1 Vanessa urtica*
*2 Cynthia cardia*

**42** *1 & 2 Catagrama condomanus*
*3 & 4 C. pyramus*

**43** *1 Nemeobius lucina*
*2 Melitaea athalia*

**44** *Saturnia isis*

1

3

2

1

3

4

2

1

5
1
2
3
4

6

7

8
1
2
3
4

9

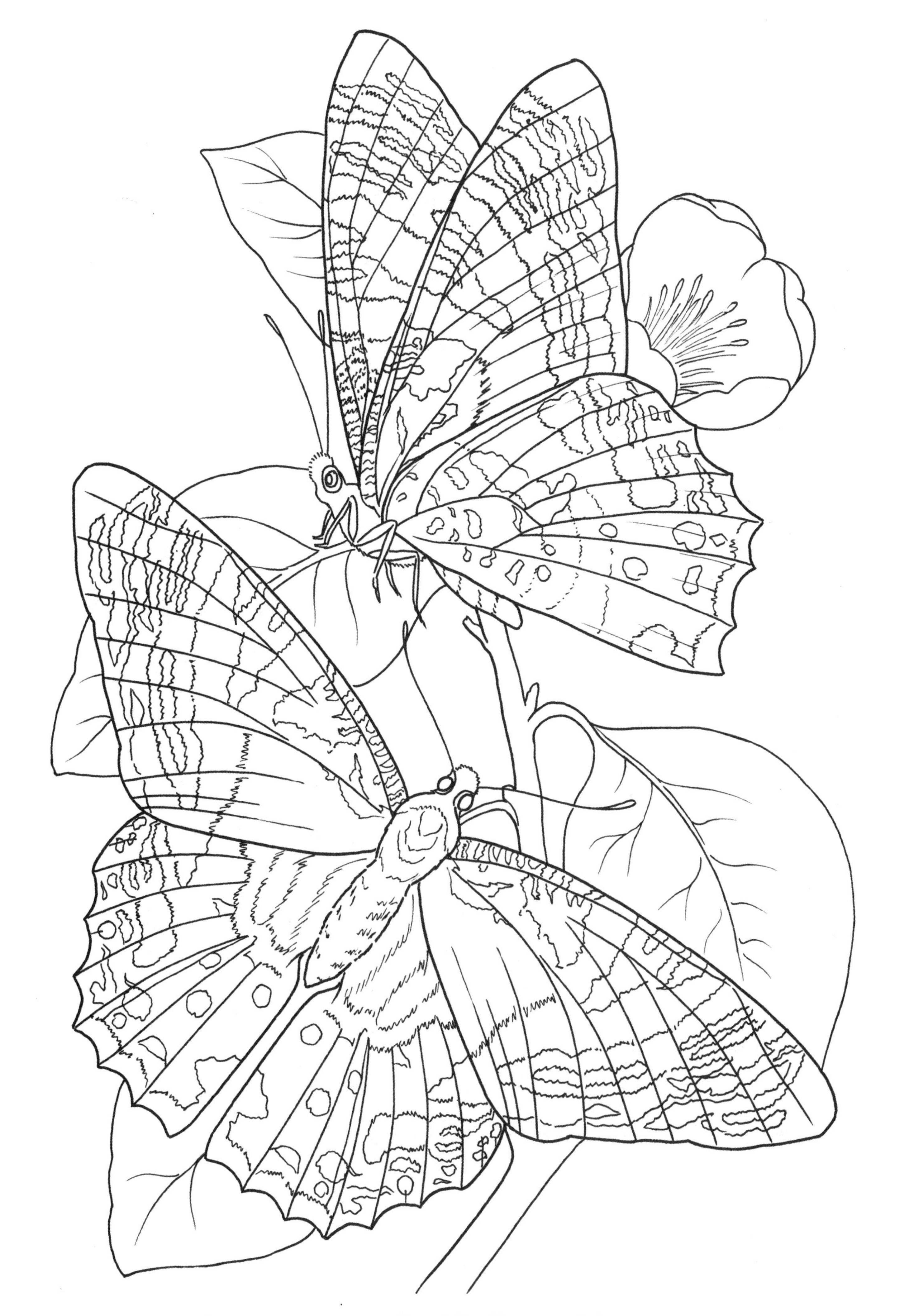

2
3
5
1
4

1

2

1

3

2

13

1
2

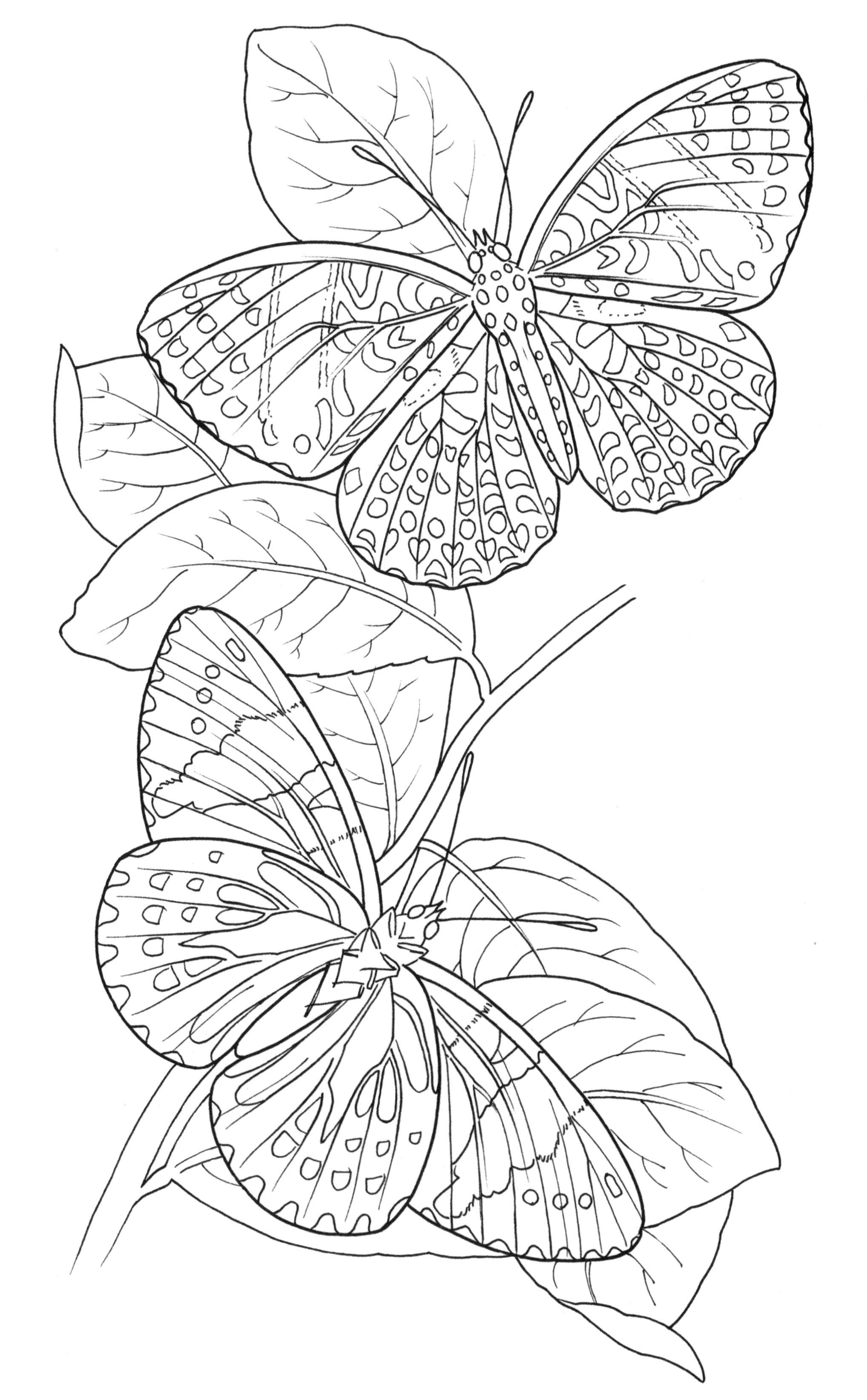

1
2

1
1
2

17

2
1
3

19

1
2

1
2
3
4

1

1

2

2

2
1

1
2
3
3

4

2

3

1

1
3
3
2
2

1
2
3

30

1
2
1
4
3
3
4

1
2

3

1

2

1
2

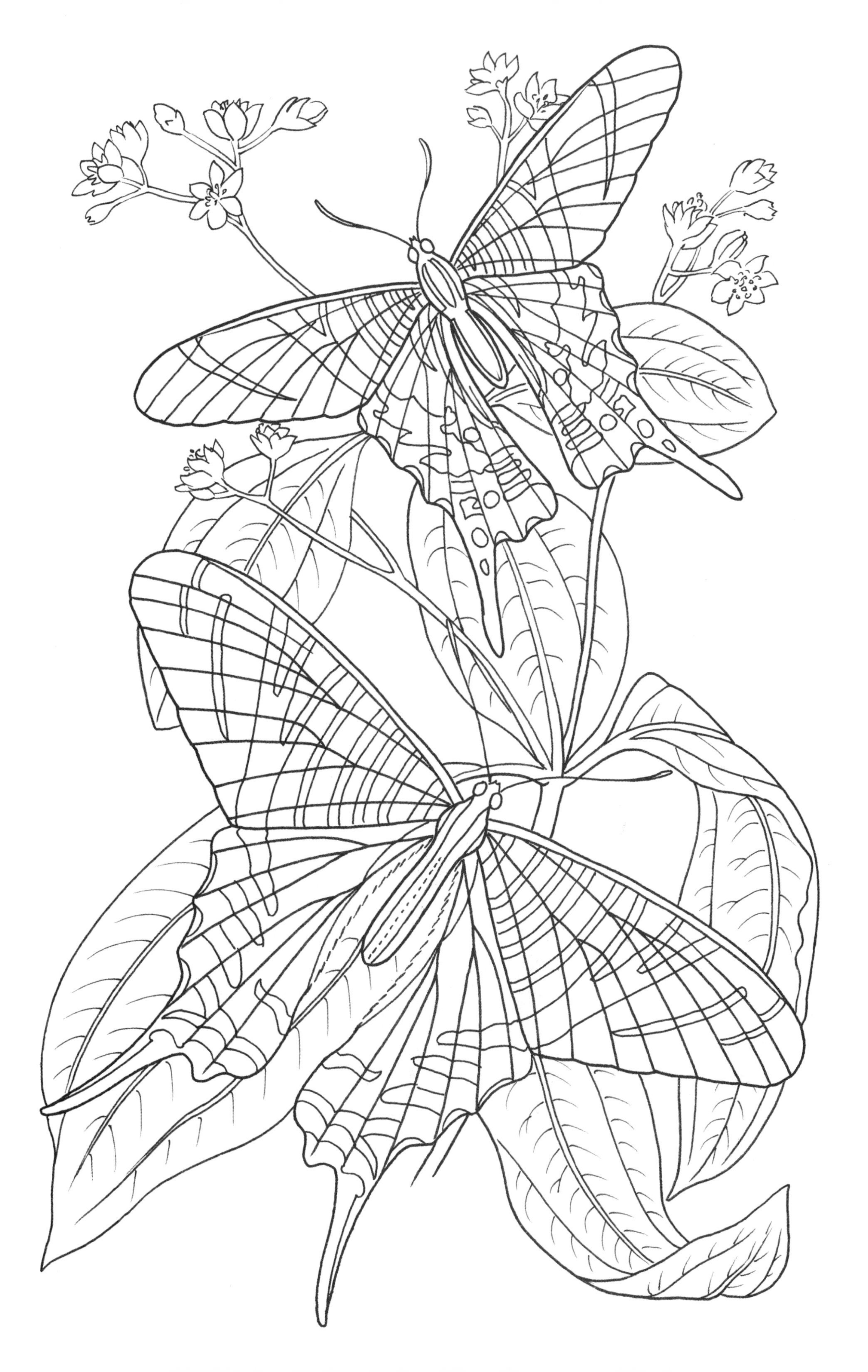

1
1
2
2
3

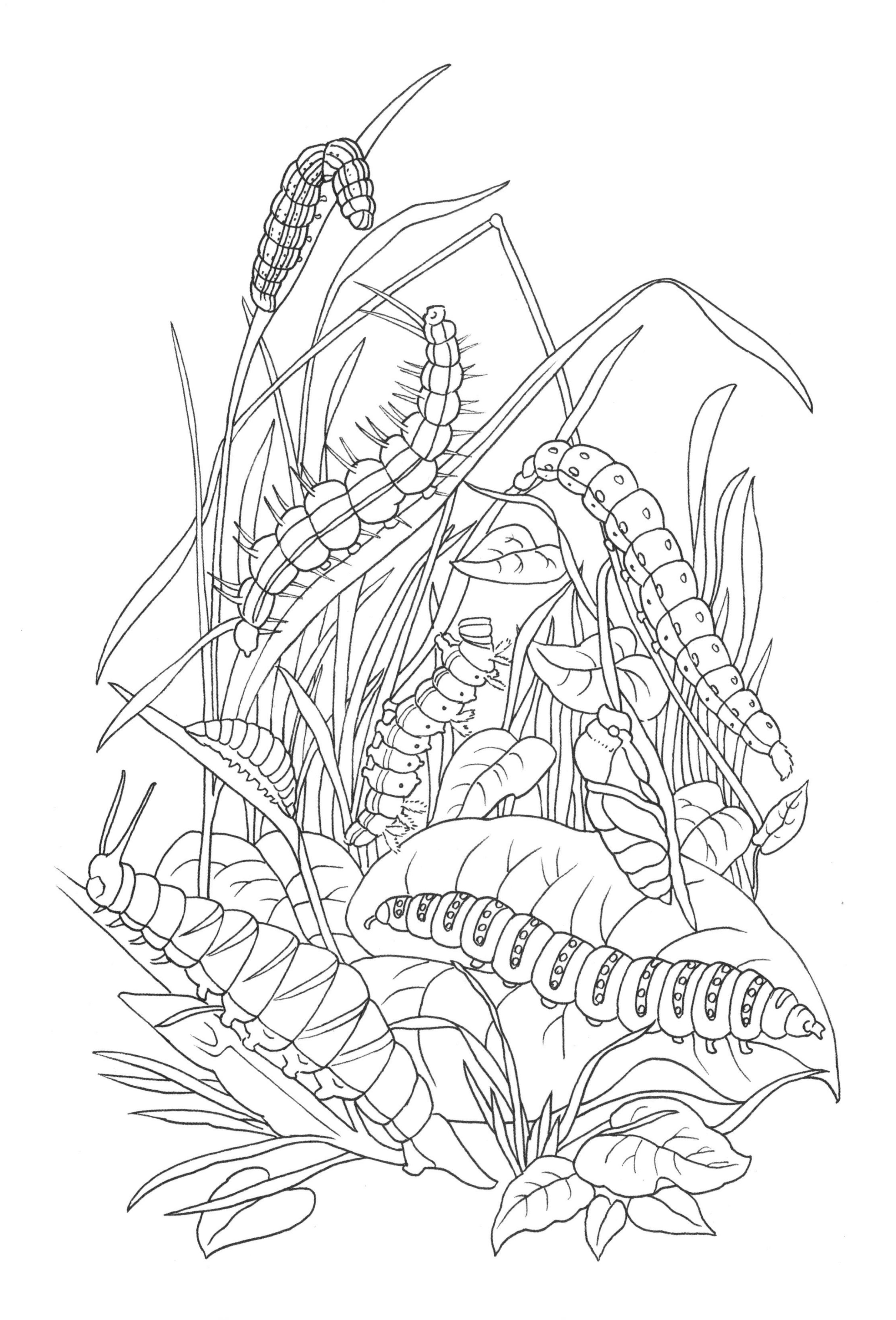

1
3
2

41

1

3

4

2

2

1

1

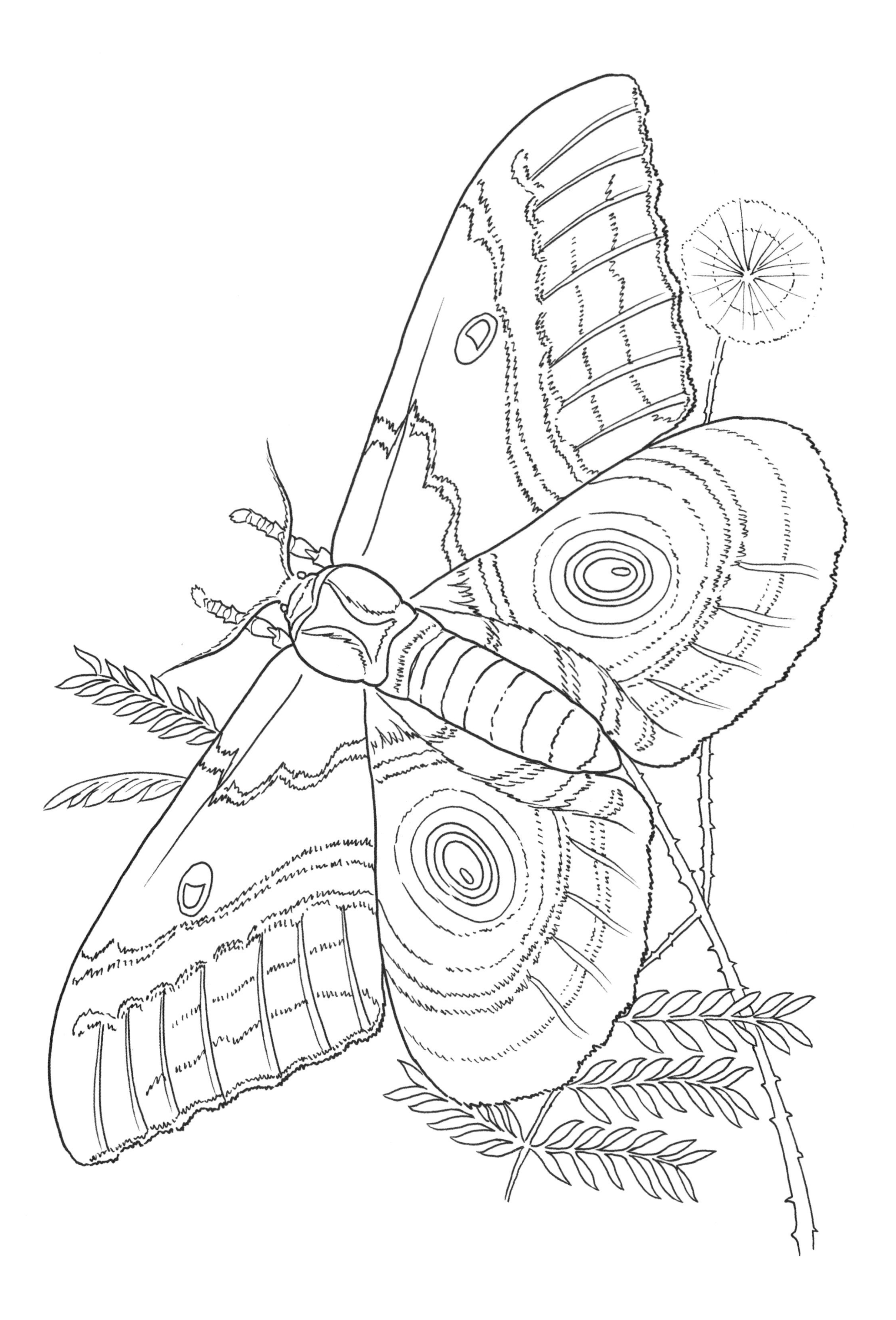